In - no-cence and peace are there. All is good that is de - sired.
Winds from that far land are blown, whis-per-ing with se - cret breath.

Fa - ces there are al - ways fair. Love grows ne - ver old nor tired.
Hope that plays her tune of love, Love that con-quers pain and death.

We shall ne - ver find that love - ly land of might-have - been. I can ne - ver
Shall we e - ver find that love - ly land of might-have - been? Will I e - ver

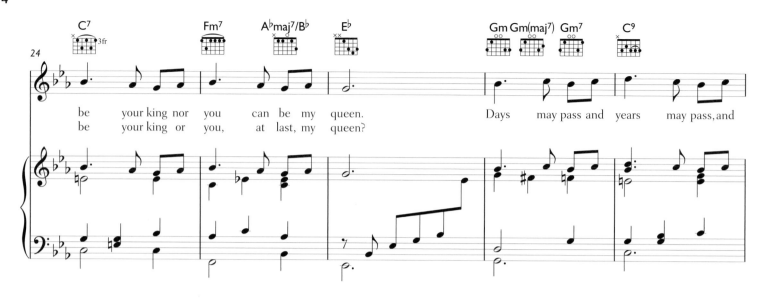

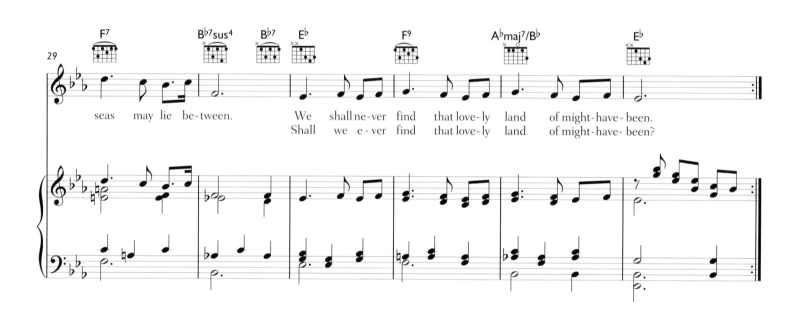

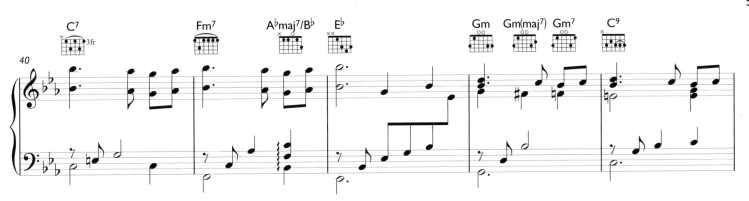

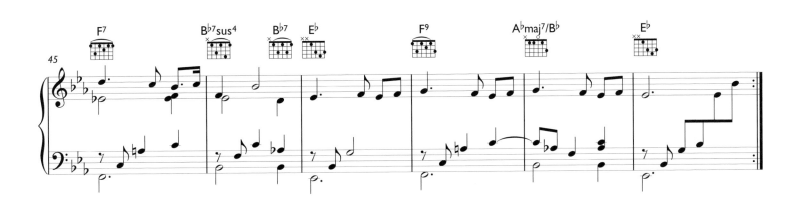

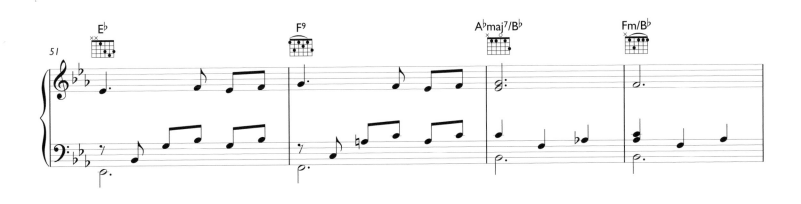

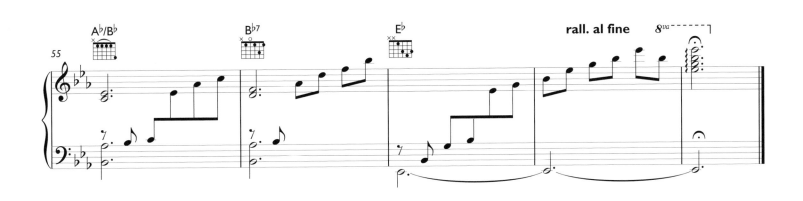

100 YEARS OF POPULAR MUSIC
FROM FABER MUSIC

				0-571-53340-X	**1900**		
0-571-53341-8	**20s Vol.1**	0-571-53345-0	**40s Vol.1**	0-571-53349-3	**60s Vol.1**	0-571-53353-1	**80s Vol.1**
0-571-53342-6	**20s Vol.2**	0-571-53346-9	**40s Vol.2**	0-571-53350-7	**60s Vol.2**	0-571-53354-X	**80s Vol.2**
0-571-53343-4	**30s Vol.1**	0-571-53347-7	**50s Vol.1**	0-571-53351-5	**70s Vol.1**	0-571-53355-8	**90s Vol.1**
0-571-53344-2	**30s Vol.2**	0-571-53348-5	**50s Vol.2**	0-571-53352-3	**70s Vol.2**	0-571-53356-6	**90s Vol.2**

FABER *ff* MUSIC

To buy Faber Music publications or to find out about the full range of titles available
please contact your local music retailer or Faber Music sales enquiries:

Faber Music Ltd, Burnt Mill, Elizabeth Way, Harlow CM20 2HX
Tel: +44 (0) 1279 82 89 82   Fax: +44 (0) 1279 82 89 83
sales@fabermusic.com   fabermusic.com   expressprintmusic.com

fabermusic.com

Printed in England by Caligraving Ltd

ISBN10:   0-571-53430-9
EAN13: 978-0-571-53430-2

The Land Of Might-Have-Been

as performed by

Jeremy Northam

Piano · Vocal · Chords

Words by Edward Moore

Music by Ivor Novello

from the *Gosford Park* Original Motion Picture Soundtrack

Decca Records

ff FABER MUSIC

The Land Of Might-Have-Been

Words by Edward Moore
Music by Ivor Novello

1. Some-where_ there's a no-ther land, diff-'rent from this world be-low.
2. Some-times_ on the rar-est nights, comes the vi-sion calm and clear.

Far more_ merc-i-ful-ly planned than the cru-el place we know.
Gleam-ing_ with un-earth-ly lights, on our path of doubt and fear.